ATTACK OF THE FARGS

and **Porridge**

Michael Thomson
Trevor Millum

Oxford University Press 1996

Attack of the Fargs

1

The Spaceship

The spaceship stopped on the far side of the Moon. Inside the ship the Fargs from Planet Farg were getting ready. This trip was the first part of the Fargs' plan to take over the Earth.

'This is my first planet take-over,' said one of the Fargs, its three green eyes blinking one after the other. 'I do hope we have some fun!'

'Fun?' said General Trunt, coming into the room. 'The take-over of the Earth will not be fun. It is for the glory of Farg!'

As he said this all the Fargs jumped up onto their three legs. They lifted up their three feelers and shouted, 'The glory of Farg!'

The General looked round. The Fargs' round bodies, rather like jellyfish, were wobbling with joy. 'What a fine team of Fargs,' he said to himself.

'Blobs of Fargs,' the General went on, 'we are here today to find out how easy it will be for us to invade. The rest of the Fleet will watch to see how we get on.'

The spaceship zipped down to Earth, and landed in the middle of London, near Park Lane.

2
Bella

As the Fargs were finding a place to land, Bella Bradshaw walked down the road. Bella was a traffic warden who loved her job. She liked keeping the streets of London safe and clear. Bella turned into Park Lane. There were a lot of meters here. Was anyone parking beyond their time limit?

Then she saw a big, silver car – except it wasn't a car because it was shaped like a saucer. It had no wheels, only sort of legs that it stood on. It had lights flashing all over it.

Bella had read about some TV show, *The Y Files* or something, that was going to be filmed in London. She strolled over. Then her heart began to beat fast. What's that? No money in the meter at all?! She reached for her book and out came her pen and the small plastic bag. She wrote the ticket and slapped it onto the... where was the windscreen? Well, she slapped it onto the side of the thing anyway.

Just then a head popped up out of the top of the whatever it was. Three green eyes blinked at Bella. She blinked her two blue ones back.

'Shree, shplut, thrink?!' the head said.

'What?' said Bella.

The head came out a little bit more. Then the top of a green and blobby body came out. 'My goodness,' Bella said to herself, 'these costumes are good!'

General Trunt, for that is who it was, took out his Earth/Fargian decoder. He plugged it in.

'Greetings, Earthlings!' he said. 'Like, what is going down here, dude?' (The decoder did not always get things quite right.)

'You've got a ticket!' said Bella.

'Tick-et?'

'Yes, ticket. I don't care what you're filming, you didn't put any money into the meter. You had better put some in or you will have to move on. And don't forget to pay the fine within two weeks.'

'Money? We have no money,' said the General.

'No money? Well, move on then. You can't park here. Move!'

The head went back inside again.

3
Double Yellows

'You see, General,' said one of the Fargs, 'you can't just park the ship anywhere.' This Farg had spent the last few years on Earth. But, as he had to pretend to be a big jellyfish, he had not seen much. He had spent most of the time at sea. He only came out at night, when he could not be seen, to snoop about. He went on, 'You have to put bits of metal, called money, into the slots. Then you can park. I think.'

The Fargian spaceship had now moved on. General Trunt did not want to make any fuss. He said, 'We must obey any strange rules. We are here to find out about the Earthlings. Our Great Fleet will destroy them later. We must keep out of the way for now.'

At last they found a place to park. There were no meters here. All they saw were two pretty yellow lines painted down the sides of the road.

Just as General Trunt started to climb out, Bella walked up. 'You can't park here,' she said. 'It's double yellow lines. Now move on or I will get you clamped!'

The General didn't know what 'clamped' was, but it sounded nasty. He went inside again. 'It seems we can't park here. Let's go...'

4
Clamps and Tow-trucks

Bella went round the corner and down Duke Street. That silver car-thing was really getting to her, and the fat green man smelt like a kipper! Now here it was again, parked by a zebra crossing. They had gone too far this time! Bella took out her mobile phone and called base. She would get the thing clamped!

The clamping did not work very well. The men could not find a wheel or any other place to put the clamp on. So Bella called up the tow-truck.

Even towing the spaceship away was a problem at first. In the end, Bella had to call

for two trucks, one at each end. They lifted the spaceship off the ground and took it away to the pound. Bella rubbed her hands with glee! It was turning out to be a good day after all.

5
Fines and Fakes

By this time the Fargians had gone. They had been pleased that they had found a place to park. 'No yellow lines, no meters,' said

General Trunt. 'Only these lovely zig-zags and black-and-white stripes on the road.'

They had, at last, worked out what 'fine' meant. 'We had better go and pay this "fine" money now,' said General Trunt. 'We must not make a fuss. If we pay the fine the Earthlings will not think that we are spies.'

The General gave his orders. Half the Fargs would go and find out about the Earthlings, the others would go with him to pay the fine. And so it was that a troop of green, jellyfish-like blobs went into the town hall.

'They must be in costume for College Rag week,' the man behind the counter said to himself. The Fargians went up to the desk and handed over the parking ticket and a cheque.

'Yes, I see,' said the man behind the desk. Then he looked at the cheque – it was from the

Bank of Farg. 'Just wait here,' the man said. He came back with a policeman.

'This cheque is not valid,' the policeman said. 'It is against the law to use fake cheques. I'm afraid you will have to come down to the police station.'

6
Fargs' Defeat

The rest of the Fargian Fleet were a short distance beyond the Solar System. They were waiting for the signal to invade. At last the Admiral of the Fleet was given the signal. He looked at it and went a pale green. He shook all over.

'Call off the Fleet,' he yelled. The Admiral's second-in-command asked why. 'Well,' the Admiral said, 'it seems General Trunt is locked up behind bars, along with half his force. The spaceship has been taken by the Earthlings, hidden or crushed in something they call "the pound". The rest of the force has gone missing, but that is not the worst.'

'What could be worse?!'

'All this was done by just one Earthling called a "traffic warden". If one Earthling can do this, what hope do we have against the rest of them? We could have all been killed. Let's leave these brutes alone.'

With those words the Fleet went into hyperdrive and sped away.

Back on Earth, Bella had saved the planet,

even if she did not know it. And the Fargians who were left here? Well, General Trunt was let off with a warning. The rest of the Fargians went on a tour of London, by bus.

They met the General back at the place where they had parked, but the spaceship was missing. Someone told them that they would only find a spaceship in the Science Museum. They got lost trying to find the museum and ended up in the Underground. They are still there now, as far as I know. So if you see any big, green jellyfish down there, don't talk about parking tickets!

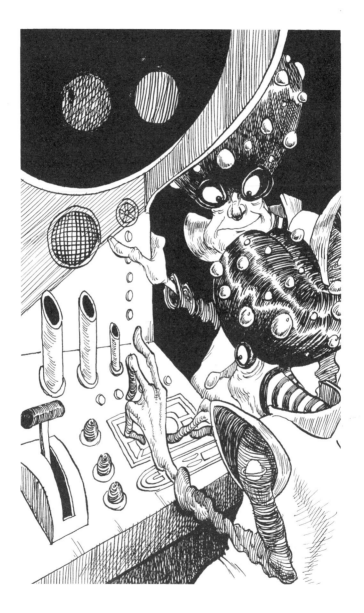

Porridge

1
Zooming In

The computer screen showed a green and blue circle. Changi and Ovsted had been watching it for a long time. The picture changed to show a town on the edge of the sea. It was early in the morning.

'Zoom in,' said Changi.

'We've seen it all before,' said Ovsted, but they zoomed in anyway. They saw streets and houses, gardens, and trees. People were walking, driving, and sitting.

Changi and Ovsted were professors of language on the planet Zircon. It was a boring job observing Earth.

'Let's hear what they are saying,' said Ovsted.

Ovsted turned up the volume. Squeaky jabber filled their ears. 'Slower,' said Changi. They slowed down the speed until each word could be heard.

'I can understand the words now,' said Ovsted. 'They don't say much.'

'They say a lot,' replied Changi.

'But nothing interesting,' said Ovsted. 'They say: Would you like a cup of tea? How do you like my hair? Isn't the weather awful?'

'We could make it more interesting,' said Changi.

Ovsted looked at him. 'How?'

'We could... make some changes.'

Ovsted frowned. 'It's not allowed.'

'But who will know? And it would help our research.'

Ovsted was tempted. 'Just a little change?'

'A very little change. I have an idea. We often talk about the importance of words and letters. So let's try something to test it out.'

'An experiment?'

'Exactly. We'll pick two human beings. Let's see now...'

Changi zoomed in on a house in a street. In the house was a bedroom and in the bedroom was a bed. In the bed was a man who was snoring. His name was Nott. Mr Nott was a teacher.

'He can be Person A,' said Changi. 'We will record his first word today. Then we will make him repeat it.'

'Not all the time,' said Ovsted. 'That would be boring.'

'No. I think every seventh word.'

'Every seventh word. Agreed.'

Changi pushed a button on the machine. 'Right.'

Ovsted zoomed in on another house and another bedroom and another sleeping figure. It was a boy called Patrick. Ovsted looked closely at the computer screen.

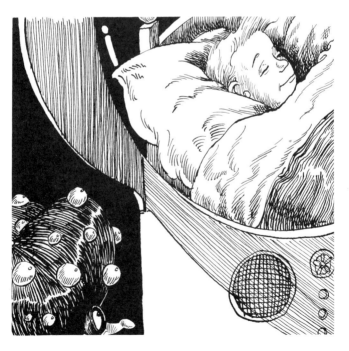

'He will do,' said Changi. 'He will be our Person B. And we will give him the letter B. He will use it over and over again.'

'How often?'

'Every seventh letter!'

And so the experiment began. Ovsted and Changi stared at the screen as day began to dawn in the town.

2
Porridge for Breakfast

Mr Nott was a teacher. He looked like a bulldog with toothache. Maybe that was why he was such a miserable teacher.

He woke up and stared at the ceiling. It was Monday morning and he had to take Year 9 assembly. He hated doing this, especially when there was nothing to grumble about.

Mr Nott's thoughts were interrupted. 'What do you want for breakfast, dear?' his wife shouted up to him.

'Porridge!' he shouted back rudely.

Changi and Ovsted looked at each other. 'The first word of the day,' said Changi. 'This should be fun.'

'A good word,' said Ovsted. 'I look forward to hearing it often.'

Mr Nott never talked much at breakfast. Mrs Nott asked him if he wanted another cup of tea. 'No,' he replied. 'I have got to take porridge this morning.'

He did not realize that when he meant to say 'assembly' he had said 'porridge'. Changi and Ovsted grinned at each other. Mrs Nott did not ask any questions. She had learnt to keep quiet over the years.

3
All Porridge and Bs

At school, Mr Nott greeted the caretaker and Miss Chuffly, the headteacher. When he greeted her, he said, 'Porridge.'

The Head was used to Mr Nott's odd ways, but she looked at him strangely and said, 'It's been a long term. It will soon be Christmas.'

'All those carols to sing and porridge to make and Christmas plays to porridge through,' grumbled Mr Nott.

The Head looked again at Mr Nott. 'I think I'll take Year 9 assembly this morning, Mr Nott,' she said. 'Better keep an eye on him,' she thought.

So Mr Nott sat in his classroom until his first Year 7 class came in. Patrick was one of them. 'Good mobning, sib,' said Pat. Pat was a cheerful boy – that was why Mr Nott did not like him.

'Morning,' said Mr Nott, without looking up at Pat. He had an unpleasant feeling that today things were not quite right, but he could not say why.

Pat sat down and got out his books. He turned to his friend Kevin. 'Have yob got a pebcil shabpener, Kbvin?' he asked. He had no idea how funny he sounded.

'Got a cold?' asked Kevin.

'I dob't think bo. My nosb is OK.'

Kevin wondered if he was having trouble

with his ears. But then Mr Nott called the class to order and told them to take out their porridge. Everyone looked up at him. 'Did I say something unusual?' he growled, raising one eyebrow.

'No, sir,' said one or two at the front.

'Then porridge you please get out your history porridge.'

Several of the class burst into giggling fits. Others wondered if Mr Nott had gone completely mad. Some thought they had missed something important the day before. Mr Nott raised his voice and both his eyebrows. 'Get out your history books!' he roared. That might have had some effect, but then he added, 'At porridge!'

There was uproar. Some of the class searched in their books to find something on porridge or the history of porridge. Others were bent over their desks, breathless with laughter, while some looked around in confusion.

Pat, always helpful, put his hand up. 'Yob see, you beep saybng porrbdge.' There was a moment of silence in the class as this latest madness was taken in.

Some thought that Pat was taking the mickey out of Mr Nott. They held their breath in fear and dread. Those who had been giggling and then laughing now fell on the floor, hardly able to breathe.

Two students were so confused that they started to do their maths homework. Another one began an essay on the subject of porridge.

Mr Nott glared at Patrick. 'What did you say, lad, eh? Porridge?'

Very unsure, but thinking that honesty was the best policy, Patrick repeated what he had said before. All the Bs made it hard to hear but Mr Nott got the meaning.

'What!' he bawled. 'I keep on saying "porridge", porridge?'

4
What is Going On?

Just then the Head looked in. She liked to keep an eye on the far corners of the school, especially when she felt something odd was going on. The noises coming from Mr Nott's classroom seemed louder and stranger than usual.

'Is this a drama lesson, Mr Nott?' she asked.

Mr Nott looked blank. He was the last person to do something creative like acting out scenes from history. Instead he said, 'This boy is being very cheeky,' and jabbed his finger towards Patrick.

The Head did not know Patrick very well but she did know that he was not the sort of boy to be rude to Mr Nott. 'Really?' she said. 'Come here, Patrick. Tell me what is going on.'

Oh dear, thought Pat. Shall I tell her the truth? He sighed. 'Misb, we just ban't undbrstand Br Nott. Hb doesn't bake senbe.' He avoided using the word 'porridge'.

Mr Nott was outraged. He went redder and redder in the face. His bristly hair stood on end. 'Porridge!' he shouted. 'This wretched child is just making porridge of me.'

'Let's talk about this in my room,' said the Head, looking at Mr Nott. 'Go and sit down, Patrick,' she said. She told the class what work they were to get on with.

In her office, the Head spoke firmly to Mr Nott. 'I don't know what the matter is with you this morning. But I think that taking your personal problems out on a poor lad who has difficulties speaking is most unkind. I suggest you go home and rest. Your classes will be covered for the rest of the day.'

Poor Mr Nott felt hard done by but he was relieved to get home. He did not feel ill but he did feel very strange.

5
Back on Zircon

Changi pushed a button on the machine and turned to Ovsted. 'You see, Nott is the one who got into trouble. Words are more important than letters. A few letters in the wrong place and no one notices. But one word in the wrong place and...'

'I think we should try the experiment again,' said Ovsted. 'But we should use some different people. Let's zoom in on another town.'

Somewhere in a school near you someone is about to start speaking very strangely. Look out, it could be you!

Oxford University Press, Walton Street, Oxford, OX2 6DP

Oxford   New York
Athens   Auckland   Bangkok   Bogota   Bombay
Buenos Aires   Calcutta   Cape Town   Dar es Salaam
Delhi   Florence   Hong Kong   Istanbul   Karachi
Kuala Lumpur   Madras   Madrid   Melbourne
Mexico City   Nairobi   Paris   Singapore
Taipei   Tokyo   Toronto

and associated companies in
Berlin   Ibadan

Oxford is a trade mark of Oxford University Press

© Michael Thomson (Attack of the Fargs) 1996
© Trevor Millum (Porridge) 1996
First published 1996

ISBN 0 19 833569 5

Printed in Great Britain

Illustrations by Adam Stower